Goal!

by Jane A C West

illustrated by Pete Smith

Titles in the  series

Level 3
Goal!	Jane A C West
Too Hot	Roger Hurn/Alison Hawes

Level 4
A Big Catch	Alison Hawes
Deyda's Drum	Roger Hurn
The Strawberry Thief	Alison Hawes
Billy's Boy	Melanie Joyce

Level 5
Cage Boy	Jillian Powell
Master Blaster	Melanie Joyce
Game Player King	Stan Cullimore
In the Zone	Tony Norman

Level 6
Dodgems	Jane A C West
Tansy Smith	Helen Orme

Level 7
Pirate Attack	Jonny Zucker
Hitting the Basket	Jonny Zucker

Badger Publishing Limited
Suite G08, Business & Technology Centre
Bessemer Drive, Stevenage, Hertfordshire, SG1 2DX
Telephone: 01438 791037 Fax: 01438 791036
www.badger-publishing.co.uk

Goal! ISBN 978 1 84691 852 0

Text © Jane A C West 2010
Complete work © Badger Publishing Limited 2010

All rights reserved. No part of this publication may be reproduced, stored in any form or by any means mechanical, electronic, recording or otherwise without the prior permission of the publisher.

The right of Jane A C West to be identified as author of this Work has been asserted by her in accordance with the Copyright, Designs and Patents Act 1988.

Publisher: David Jamieson
Editor: Danny Pearson
Design: Fiona Grant
Illustration: Pete Smith
Printed and bound in China through Colorcraft Ltd., Hong Kong

Contents

Story 1
Goal! 4
Questions 13

Story 2
Lost Dog 14
Questions 23

Story 3
Music! Muzyka! 24
Questions 32

Badger Publishing

Story 1
Goal!

Vocabulary

Park   Understand
Fast   School
Player/Players Team
Scored   Smiled

Main Characters

This is Aban. He is from Iraq.

There were ten boys.

They were in the park.

They wanted to play football.

They saw Aban.

"Come and play football with us!"

Aban smiled. "Football!"

Aban got the ball.

He ran very fast.

He ran past one player.

He ran past two players.

He scored!

"Goal!"

"You are very good at football."

Aban smiled. "Football!"

"You must play on the team at school."

Aban frowned.

He did not understand.

"Football?"

"Yes," said the boy.

"You must play on the football team at school."

Aban smiled. "Football! Goal!"

Questions

Why did the boys ask Aban to play football with them?

Was Aban good at football?

What happened next?

What country is Aban from?

Story 2
Lost Dog

Vocabulary

Lonely
Friends
Wagged
Lost

Straight
Turned
Home

Main Characters

Rafal

Billy

Rafal was sad.

He was sad because he was lonely.

He was lonely because he had no friends.
Rafal sat down.

"I wish I had a friend."

Rafal was not alone.

A small dog sat down.

The dog had sad eyes.

"Who are you?"

"Hello, Billy!"

The dog wagged his tail.

"Are you lost?"

Billy wagged his tail.

"I must take you to your home."

Billy and Rafal walked down the street.

They turned left. They turned right.

They walked straight on.

Rafal saw a girl.

She looked sad.

When she saw Billy she smiled.

"Billy! Where did you go? Did you get lost?"

"Thank you for finding, Billy," she said.

"You are very kind."

She smiled.

Billy wagged his tail.

Rafal did not feel lonely any more.

Questions

Why was Rafal sad?

Who did he meet?

Why didn't Rafal feel sad any more?

What is your favourite animal?

Story 3
Music! Muzyka!

New Words
Like/Liked
Music/Muzyka
Listening/Listened
Britain/Poland/Somalia

Nodded
Tapped
Clicked
iPod

Main Characters

Telek - He is from Poland

Nadif - He is from Somalia

Telek liked music.

He liked listening to music on his iPod.

He clicked his fingers.

He nodded his head.

He tapped his foot.

Music made Telek feel good.

He liked music from Britain.

He liked music from Poland (muzyka).
There was a new boy at school.

His name was Nadif.

Nadif was lonely.

He did not have any friends.

Nadif was watching Telek.

"Hello, Nadif."

"Do you like music?"

Nadif nodded.
They listened to music together.

Telek had lots of songs on his iPod.

Telek clicked his fingers.

Nadif tapped his foot.

They both smiled.

They listened to music from Britain.

They listened to music from Poland.
"Tomorrow we can listen to music from Somalia," said Telek.

Nadif smiled. "Muzyka!"

Telek smiled, too.

Questions

Where is this story set?

What was Telek doing?

Why did he share his iPod with Nadif?

What music would you have on an iPod playlist?